Maths
made easy

Key Stage 2 lower
ages 7-9
Subtraction

Author
Peter Gash

Consultant
David Clemson

LONDON • NEW YORK • SYDNEY • DELHI

Word problems

When you see these words, they usually mean that you have to subtract.

take away   *subtract*   *how many are left*
how much less   *difference between*   *minus*
how many more is   *how many more to make*

Write the answers in the boxes.

What is   [slugs]   take away   [slugs]   ?   □

How many are left if you take   [snails]   from   [snails]   ?   □

What is   [beetles]   minus   [beetles]   ?   □

What is the difference between   [bees]   and   [bees]   ?   □

How many more is   [dragonflies]   than   [dragonflies]   ?   □

How much less is   [ants]   than   [ants]   ?   □

What does   [grubs]   subtract   [grub]   leave?   □

Subtraction signs

You can use signs to write subtractions.

− is the sign for *subtract*.

= is the sign for *equals*.

Write − and = to make these subtractions true.

3 ☐ 8 ☐ 5   7 ☐ 1 ☐ 6

4 ☐ 1 ☐ 3   9 ☐ 2 ☐ 7

3 ☐ 9 ☐ 6   6 ☐ 8 ☐ 2

9 ☐ 5 ☐ 4   6 ☐ 5 ☐ 1

4 ☐ 8 ☐ 4   9 ☐ 6 ☐ 3

7 ☐ 5 ☐ 2   10 ☐ 4 ☐ 6

8 ☐ 9 ☐ 1   5 ☐ 8 ☐ 3

Subtraction signs

Write – and = to make these subtractions true.

1 ☐ 6 ☐ 5   8 ☐ 2 ☐ 6

2 ☐ 7 ☐ 5   7 ☐ 9 ☐ 2

9 ☐ 5 ☐ 4   9 ☐ 10 ☐ 1

7 ☐ 2 ☐ 5   3 ☐ 1 ☐ 2

5 ☐ 1 ☐ 4   9 ☐ 8 ☐ 1

5 ☐ 10 ☐ 5   1 ☐ 9 ☐ 8

1 ☐ 8 ☐ 7   6 ☐ 3 ☐ 3

4 ☐ 1 ☐ 3   8 ☐ 5 ☐ 3

5 ☐ 8 ☐ 3   2 ☐ 1 ☐ 1

7 ☐ 4 ☐ 3   9 ☐ 6 ☐ 3

Smaller and bigger numbers

Subtracting makes numbers smaller. Adding makes numbers bigger.
Write whether the answers to these problems will be *bigger* or *smaller*.

I had 40p. I gave my sister 10p.
The amount I have now is…

My puppy was 30 cm long. It grew
another 10 cm. My puppy is now…

There were 30 cakes. 15 were sold.
The number of cakes left is…

16 boys were playing football. 4 went
home. The number of boys playing is…

I had 10 pencils. My friend gave me
4 more. The number of pencils I have is…

There were 20 sweets in a box. I ate 3.
The number of sweets left is…

My brother had 70p. I gave him 30p.
The amount he has now is…

Money problems

Write the answers.

What is   take away   ?

What is left if you take from ?

What is minus ?

What is the difference between and ?

How many more is   than   ?

How much less is than   ?

What is left when you subtract   from ?

What is   minus   ?

Counting back to subtract

When you subtract numbers, it can help to start with the largest number and then count back.

$$18 - 6 = 12$$

18: 17, 16, 15, 14, 13, 12

Start with the larger number and count back to find the answer. Show your counting back in the long boxes.

15 − 5 = [ ]

[   ]

19 − 4 = [ ]

[   ]

17 − 6 = [ ]

[   ]

18 − 4 = [ ]

[   ]

16 − 8 = [ ]

[   ]

23 − 8 = [ ]

[   ]

19 − 7 = [ ]

[   ]

24 − 7 = [ ]

[   ]

Subtracting two-digit numbers

When you do a subtraction with two-digit numbers, like 29 − 17, it can help to write them out vertically like this:

$$
\begin{array}{r}
\text{T U} \\
2\ 9 \\
-\ 1\ 7 \\
\hline
1\ 2 \\
\hline
\end{array}
$$

This way, you can subtract the units and tens separately.

Write these subtractions out vertically, then write the answers.

26 − 11 = ☐

    T U

    ——

27 − 13 = ☐

    T U

    ——

28 − 16 = ☐

    T U

    ——

29 − 14 = ☐

    T U

    ——

Speed check

Write the answers to these subtractions. Do as many as you can in two minutes. Can you see any patterns?

11 – 2 = ☐   12 – 5 = ☐   13 – 9 = ☐

11 – 3 = ☐   12 – 6 = ☐   14 – 5 = ☐

11 – 4 = ☐   12 – 7 = ☐   14 – 6 = ☐

11 – 5 = ☐   12 – 8 = ☐   14 – 7 = ☐

11 – 6 = ☐   12 – 9 = ☐   14 – 8 = ☐

11 – 7 = ☐   13 – 4 = ☐   14 – 9 = ☐

11 – 8 = ☐   13 – 5 = ☐   15 – 6 = ☐

11 – 9 = ☐   13 – 6 = ☐   15 – 7 = ☐

12 – 3 = ☐   13 – 7 = ☐   15 – 8 = ☐

12 – 4 = ☐   13 – 8 = ☐   15 – 9 = ☐

Counting back to subtract

When you subtract numbers, it can help to start with the largest number and count back. For example, for 118 – 6 count back 6 from 118:

118: 117, 116, 115, 114, 113, 112

The answer is 112.

Start with the larger number and count back to find the answer. Show your counting back in the long boxes.

115 – 5 = ☐

219 – 4 = ☐

178 – 6 = ☐

162 – 8 = ☐

181 – 4 = ☐

235 – 7 = ☐

119 – 7 = ☐

214 – 6 = ☐

Subtracting units from hundreds

When you subtract a single-digit number like 5 from a hundreds number like 248, often only the units change:

```
  H T U
  2 4 8
-     5
  ‾‾‾‾‾
  2 4 3
  ‾‾‾‾‾
```

The tens and hundreds remain the same.

Work out these subtractions.

$218 - 5 =$ ⬚ $256 - 5 =$ ⬚

$289 - 7 =$ ⬚ $477 - 4 =$ ⬚

$473 - 1 =$ ⬚ $586 - 5 =$ ⬚

$256 - 3 =$ ⬚ $795 - 2 =$ ⬚

$124 - 2 =$ ⬚ $269 - 8 =$ ⬚

$375 - 3 =$ ⬚ $538 - 3 =$ ⬚

$273 - 3 =$ ⬚ $742 - 2 =$ ⬚

Subtracting units from hundreds

When you subtract a single-digit number like 6 from a hundreds number like 200, the hundreds, tens and units change:

$$\begin{array}{r} \text{H T U} \\ 2\ 0\ 0 \\ -\ \ \ \ 6 \\ \hline 1\ 9\ 4 \end{array}$$

Work out these subtractions.

200 − 5 = ☐   500 − 5 = ☐

400 − 7 = ☐   900 − 9 = ☐

500 − 1 = ☐   300 − 6 = ☐

100 − 4 = ☐   800 − 2 = ☐

600 − 2 = ☐   200 − 8 = ☐

300 − 3 = ☐   400 − 3 = ☐

700 − 6 = ☐   100 − 2 = ☐

800 − 9 = ☐   600 − 4 = ☐

Counting on to subtract

You can use a number line to subtract larger numbers. You do it by counting on and adding up the jumps:

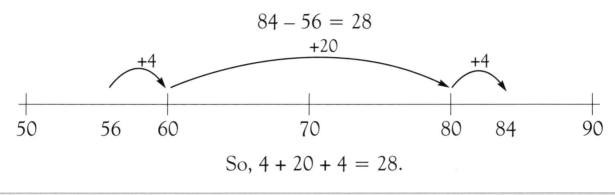

So, 4 + 20 + 4 = 28.

Fill in these number lines as you count on in jumps. Then add up the jumps.

76 – 48 = [   ]

82 – 35 = [   ]

85 – 49 = [   ]

Counting back to subtract

You can use a number line to subtract larger numbers. You do it by counting back and adding up the jumps:

$$73 - 56 = 17$$

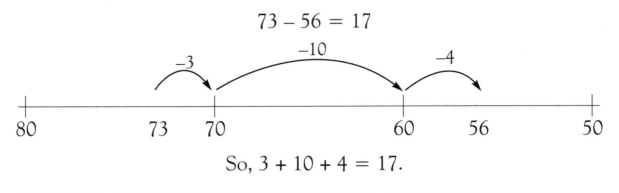

So, 3 + 10 + 4 = 17.

Fill in these number lines as you count back in jumps. Then add up the jumps.

65 − 48 = ☐

71 − 35 = ☐

71 − 35 = ☐

54 − 28 = ☐

Breaking up numbers

You can break up numbers to make them easier to subtract. For example:

$$71 - 57 = 14$$

$$71 = 70 + 1 = 60 + 11$$
$$- 57 = 50 + 7 = 50 + 7$$
$$= \underline{10 + 4} = 14$$

Break up the numbers into tens and units to subtract them. Write the answers.

43 − 29 = ☐

43 = ☐ + ☐ = ☐ + ☐

− 29 = ☐ + ☐ = ☐ + ☐

= ☐ + ☐ = ☐

84 − 36 = ☐

84 = ☐ + ☐ = ☐ + ☐

− 36 = ☐ + ☐ = ☐ + ☐

= ☐ + ☐ = ☐

Numbers ending in 1

When you subtract numbers ending in 1, it is usually quicker to take away the tens first and then the 1. For example:

$$36 - 21$$

$36 - 20 = 16 \ (-1)$. The answer is 15.

Subtract these numbers.

$33 - 11 = \boxed{}$ $85 - 51 = \boxed{}$

$48 - 21 = \boxed{}$ $65 - 41 = \boxed{}$

$52 - 41 = \boxed{}$ $96 - 51 = \boxed{}$

$25 - 21 = \boxed{}$ $88 - 61 = \boxed{}$

$44 - 31 = \boxed{}$ $67 - 31 = \boxed{}$

$26 - 11 = \boxed{}$ $42 - 11 = \boxed{}$

$37 - 21 = \boxed{}$ $63 - 31 = \boxed{}$

$69 - 51 = \boxed{}$ $54 - 11 = \boxed{}$

Answer Section

Key Stage 2 lower
Ages 7–9
Subtraction

As your child finishes each page, check the answers together. Your child may like to stick a gold star at the top of each completed page as well as on the progress chart at the beginning of the book.

2

Word problems

When you see these words, they usually mean that you have to subtract.

take away   subtract   how many are left
how much less   difference between   minus
how many more is   how many more to make

Write the answers in the boxes.

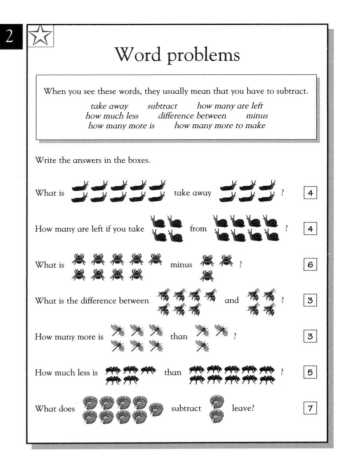

What is [🐌🐌🐌🐌🐌🐌🐌] take away [🐌🐌🐌] ? **4**

How many are left if you take [🐌🐌] from [🐌🐌🐌🐌🐌🐌] ? **4**

What is [🪲🪲🪲🪲🪲🪲🪲🪲] minus [🪲🪲] ? **6**

What is the difference between [🐜🐜🐜🐜🐜] and [🐜🐜] ? **3**

How many more is [🪰🪰🪰🪰🪰] than [🪰🪰] ? **3**

How much less is [🐜🐜🐜] than [🐜🐜🐜🐜🐜🐜🐜🐜] ? **5**

What does [🐚🐚🐚🐚🐚🐚🐚🐚] subtract [🐚] leave? **7**

3

Subtraction signs

You can use signs to write subtractions.

– is the sign for *subtract*.
= is the sign for *equals*.

Write – and = to make these subtractions true.

3 = 8 – 5   7 – 1 = 6

4 – 1 = 3   9 – 2 = 7

3 = 9 – 6   6 = 8 – 2

9 – 5 = 4   6 – 5 = 1

4 = 8 – 4   9 – 6 = 3

7 – 5 = 2   10 – 4 = 6

8 = 9 – 1   5 = 8 – 3

4

Subtraction signs

Write – and = to make these subtractions true.

1 = 6 – 5   8 – 2 = 6

2 = 7 – 5   7 = 9 – 2

9 – 5 = 4   9 = 10 – 1

7 – 2 = 5   3 – 1 = 2

5 – 1 = 4   9 – 8 = 1

5 = 10 – 5   1 = 9 – 8

1 = 8 – 7   6 – 3 = 3

4 – 1 = 3   8 – 5 = 3

5 = 8 – 3   2 – 1 = 1

7 – 4 = 3   9 – 6 = 3

Smaller and bigger numbers

Subtracting makes numbers smaller. Adding makes numbers bigger.
Write whether the answers to these problems will be *bigger* or *smaller*.

I had 40p. I gave my sister 10p.
The amount I have now is…   smaller

My puppy was 30 cm long. It grew
another 10 cm. My puppy is now…   bigger

There were 30 cakes. 15 were sold.
The number of cakes left is…   smaller

16 boys were playing football. 4 went
home. The number of boys playing is… smaller

I had 10 pencils. My friend gave me
4 more. The number of pencils I have is… bigger

There were 20 sweets in a box. I ate 3.
The number of sweets left is…   smaller

My brother had 70p. I gave him 30p.
The amount he has now is…   bigger

Money problems

Write the answers.

What is take away ?   6p

What is left if you take from ?   5p

What is minus ?   3p

What is the difference between and ? 9p

How many more is than ?   4p

How much less is than ?   8p

What is left when you subtract from ? 2p

What is minus ?   7p

Counting back to subtract

When you subtract numbers, it can help to start with the largest number
and then count back.

$$18 - 6 = 12$$

18: 17, 16, 15, 14, 13, 12

Start with the larger number and count back to find the answer. Show your
counting back in the long boxes.

$15 - 5 =$ [10]

15: 14, 13, 12, 11, 10

$19 - 4 =$ [15]

19: 18, 17, 16, 15

$17 - 6 =$ [11]

17: 16, 15, 14, 13, 12, 11

$18 - 4 =$ [14]

18: 17, 16, 15, 14

$16 - 8 =$ [8]

16: 15, 14, 13, 12, 11, 10, 9, 8

$23 - 8 =$ [15]

23: 22, 21, 20, 19, 18, 17, 16, 15

$19 - 7 =$ [12]

19: 18, 17, 16, 15, 14, 13, 12

$24 - 7 =$ [17]

24: 23, 22, 21, 20, 19, 18, 17

Subtracting two-digit numbers

When you do a subtraction with two-digit numbers, like 29 – 17, it can
help to write them out vertically like this:

```
  T U
  2 9
- 1 7
  1 2
```

This way, you can subtract the units and tens separately.

Write these subtractions out vertically, then write the answers.

$26 - 11 =$ [15]

```
  T U
  2 6
- 1 1
  1 5
```

$27 - 13 =$ [14]

```
  T U
  2 7
- 1 3
  1 4
```

$28 - 16 =$ [12]

```
  T U
  2 8
- 1 6
  1 2
```

$29 - 14 =$ [15]

```
  T U
  2 9
- 1 4
  1 5
```

Speed check

Write the answers to these subtractions. Do as many as you can in two minutes. Can you see any patterns?

11 – 2 = 9	12 – 5 = 7	13 – 9 = 4
11 – 3 = 8	12 – 6 = 6	14 – 5 = 9
11 – 4 = 7	12 – 7 = 5	14 – 6 = 8
11 – 5 = 6	12 – 8 = 4	14 – 7 = 7
11 – 6 = 5	12 – 9 = 3	14 – 8 = 6
11 – 7 = 4	13 – 4 = 9	14 – 9 = 5
11 – 8 = 3	13 – 5 = 8	15 – 6 = 9
11 – 9 = 2	13 – 6 = 7	15 – 7 = 8
12 – 3 = 9	13 – 7 = 6	15 – 8 = 7
12 – 4 = 8	13 – 8 = 5	15 – 9 = 6

Counting back to subtract

When you subtract numbers, it can help to start with the largest number and count back. For example, for 118 – 6 count back 6 from 118:

118: 117, 116, 115, 114, 113, 112

The answer is 112.

Start with the larger number and count back to find the answer. Show your counting back in the long boxes.

115 – 5 = 110

115: 114, 113, 112, 111, 110

219 – 4 = 215

219: 218, 217, 216, 215

178 – 6 = 172

178: 177, 176, 175, 174, 173, 172

162 – 8 = 154

162: 161, 160, 159, 158, 157, 156, 155, 154

181 – 4 = 177

181: 180, 179, 178, 177

235 – 7 = 228

235: 234, 233, 232, 231, 230, 229, 228

119 – 7 = 112

119: 118, 117, 116, 115, 114, 113, 112

214 – 6 = 208

214: 213, 212, 211, 210, 209, 208

Subtracting units from hundreds

When you subtract a single-digit number like 5 from a hundreds number like 248, often only the units change:

```
  H T U
  2 4 8
-     5
  2 4 3
```

The tens and hundreds remain the same.

Work out these subtractions.

218 – 5 = 213	256 – 5 = 251
289 – 7 = 282	477 – 4 = 473
473 – 1 = 472	586 – 5 = 581
256 – 3 = 253	795 – 2 = 793
124 – 2 = 122	269 – 8 = 261
375 – 3 = 372	538 – 3 = 535
273 – 3 = 270	742 – 2 = 740

Subtracting units from hundreds

When you subtract a single-digit number like 6 from a hundreds number like 200, the hundreds, tens and units change:

```
  H T U
  2 0 0
-     6
  1 9 4
```

Work out these subtractions.

200 – 5 = 195	500 – 5 = 495
400 – 7 = 393	900 – 9 = 891
500 – 1 = 499	300 – 6 = 294
100 – 4 = 96	800 – 2 = 798
600 – 2 = 598	200 – 8 = 192
300 – 3 = 297	400 – 3 = 397
700 – 6 = 694	100 – 2 = 98
800 – 9 = 791	600 – 4 = 596

Counting on to subtract

You can use a number line to subtract larger numbers. You do it by counting on and adding up the jumps:

$$84 - 56 = 28$$

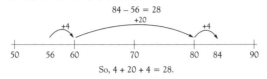

So, 4 + 20 + 4 = 28.

Fill in these number lines as you count on in jumps. Then add up the jumps.

76 – 48 = **28**

82 – 35 = **47**

85 – 49 = **36**

Counting back to subtract

You can use a number line to subtract larger numbers. You do it by counting back and adding up the jumps:

$$73 - 56 = 17$$

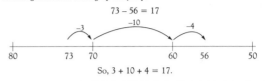

So, 3 + 10 + 4 = 17.

Fill in these number lines as you count back in jumps. Then add up the jumps.

65 – 48 = **17**

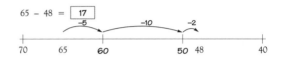

71 – 35 = **36**

54 – 28 = **26**

☆

Breaking up numbers

You can break up numbers to make them easier to subtract. For example:

$$71 - 57 = 14$$

$$71 = 70 + 1 = 60 + 11$$
$$-\ 57 = 50 + 7 = \underline{50 + 7}$$
$$= \underline{10 + 4} = 14$$

Break up the numbers into tens and units to subtract them. Write the answers.

43 – 29 = **14**

43 = **40** + **3** = **30** + **13**

– 29 = **20** + **9** = **20** + **9**

= **10** + **4** = **14**

84 – 36 = **48**

84 = **80** + **4** = **70** + **14**

– 36 = **30** + **6** = **30** + **6**

= **40** + **8** = **48**

☆

Numbers ending in 1

When you subtract numbers ending in 1, it is usually quicker to take away the tens first and then the 1. For example:

$$36 - 21$$

36 – 20 = 16 (–1). The answer is 15.

Subtract these numbers.

33 – 11 = **22**   85 – 51 = **34**

48 – 21 = **27**   65 – 41 = **24**

52 – 41 = **11**   96 – 51 = **45**

25 – 21 = **4**   88 – 61 = **27**

44 – 31 = **13**   67 – 31 = **36**

26 – 11 = **15**   42 – 11 = **31**

37 – 21 = **16**   63 – 31 = **32**

69 – 51 = **18**   54 – 11 = **43**

17

Numbers ending in 9

When you subtract numbers ending in 9 from a three-digit number, it is usually quicker to change the 9 to the nearest 10 and then add 1 to the answer. For example:

$$136 - 9$$
$$136 - 10 = 126 \ (+1). \text{ The answer is } 127.$$

Subtract these numbers.

$133 - 9 = \boxed{124}$　　　$242 - 29 = \boxed{213}$

$248 - 19 = \boxed{229}$　　　$565 - 29 = \boxed{536}$

$452 - 29 = \boxed{423}$　　　$456 - 19 = \boxed{437}$

$325 - 9 = \boxed{316}$　　　$388 - 9 = \boxed{379}$

$244 - 19 = \boxed{225}$　　　$167 - 19 = \boxed{148}$

$126 - 9 = \boxed{117}$　　　$542 - 29 = \boxed{513}$

$537 - 19 = \boxed{518}$　　　$263 - 19 = \boxed{244}$

$462 - 9 = \boxed{453}$　　　$371 - 9 = \boxed{362}$

18

Subtracting hundreds

It is as easy to subtract hundreds numbers as it is to subtract units. The answers always end in at least two zeros.

$$1400 - 700 = 700$$

Work out these subtractions.

$1400 - 800 = \boxed{600}$　　　$1100 - \boxed{900} = 200$

$1500 - 700 = \boxed{800}$　　　$1800 - \boxed{900} = 900$

$1200 - \boxed{900} = 300$　　　$1500 - 800 = \boxed{700}$

$1300 - \boxed{800} = 500$　　　$1400 - 900 = \boxed{500}$

$1600 - 900 = \boxed{700}$　　　$1600 - \boxed{800} = 800$

$1500 - 600 = \boxed{900}$　　　$1400 - \boxed{700} = 700$

$1400 - \boxed{900} = 500$　　　$1200 - 800 = \boxed{400}$

$1600 - \boxed{700} = 900$　　　$1300 - 600 = \boxed{700}$

$1500 - 900 = \boxed{600}$　　　$1100 - \boxed{300} = 800$

$1700 - 800 = \boxed{900}$　　　$1300 - \boxed{700} = 600$

19

Adding and subtracting

When you add two small numbers, sometimes they make more than 10. It can help to think of a pair of numbers that make 10 and break up the second number to make the pair.

$$6 + 7 = 13$$
$$6 + 4 \ (+ 3) = 10 + 3 = 13$$

When you subtract numbers, you can break up the second number to bring the bigger number down to 10.

$$13 - 5 = 8$$
$$(13 - 3) - 2 = 10 - 2 = 8$$

Write the answers to these problems. Look carefully at the signs.

$5 + 8 = \boxed{13}$　　　$11 - \boxed{4} = 7$

$5 + \boxed{9} = 14$　　　$16 - 8 = \boxed{8}$

$7 + 8 = \boxed{15}$　　　$\boxed{11} - 7 = 4$

$9 + \boxed{8} = 17$　　　$17 - 9 = \boxed{8}$

$5 + 7 = \boxed{12}$　　　$16 - \boxed{7} = 9$

$8 + \boxed{4} = 12$　　　$14 - 6 = \boxed{8}$

$7 + 6 = \boxed{13}$　　　$\boxed{18} - 9 = 9$

20

Adding and subtracting

When you add a small number to a bigger number, sometimes they cross the next ten. It can help to break up the small number to take the bigger number up to the next ten:

$$34 + 8 = 42$$
$$(34 + 6) + 2 = 40 + 2 = 42$$

When you subtract numbers, you can also break up the small number to bring the bigger number down to the nearest ten:

$$72 - 9 = 63$$
$$(72 - 2) - 7 = 70 - 7 = 63$$

Write the missing numbers. Look carefully at the signs.

$24 + 7 = \boxed{31}$　　　$63 - 5 = \boxed{58}$

$37 + \boxed{5} = 42$　　　$46 - \boxed{7} = 39$

$43 + 8 = \boxed{51}$　　　$54 - 6 = \boxed{48}$

$58 + \boxed{7} = 65$　　　$81 - \boxed{7} = 74$

$65 + 9 = \boxed{74}$　　　$35 - 7 = \boxed{28}$

$36 + \boxed{5} = 41$　　　$74 - \boxed{7} = 67$

$44 + 8 = \boxed{52}$　　　$92 - 9 = \boxed{83}$

Subtracting 10, 100 or 1000

When you subtract 10 from a number, only the tens change.
$$5639 - 10 = 5629$$

When you subtract 100 from a number, only the hundreds change.
$$5639 - 100 = 5539$$

When you subtract 1000 from a number, only the thousands change.
$$5639 - 1000 = 4639$$

Write the answers to these questions.

What is 100 less than 3715? 3615

What is 10 less than 3715? 3705

What is 1000 less than 3715? 2715

What is 1000 less than 6423? 5423

What is 10 less than 8179? 8169

What is 100 less than 4812? 4712

What is 1000 less than 2184? 1184

Speed check

Subtract the numbers and write the answers. Work as quickly as you can. Time yourself.

$18 - 3 = \boxed{15}$ $19 - 4 = \boxed{15}$ $14 - 9 = \boxed{5}$

$16 - 9 = \boxed{7}$ $15 - 5 = \boxed{10}$ $12 - 6 = \boxed{6}$

$19 - 6 = \boxed{13}$ $17 - 8 = \boxed{9}$ $14 - 8 = \boxed{6}$

$20 - 7 = \boxed{13}$ $16 - 7 = \boxed{9}$ $17 - 9 = \boxed{8}$

$17 - 6 = \boxed{11}$ $18 - 9 = \boxed{9}$ $20 - 9 = \boxed{11}$

$13 - 7 = \boxed{6}$ $11 - 5 = \boxed{6}$ $15 - 6 = \boxed{9}$

$15 - 8 = \boxed{7}$ $16 - 6 = \boxed{10}$ $13 - 6 = \boxed{7}$

$16 - 8 = \boxed{8}$ $13 - 8 = \boxed{5}$ $18 - 8 = \boxed{10}$

$11 - 9 = \boxed{2}$ $14 - 7 = \boxed{7}$ $20 - 8 = \boxed{12}$

$17 - 5 = \boxed{12}$ $12 - 9 = \boxed{3}$ $13 - 9 = \boxed{4}$

How long did this take you?

Subtracting large numbers

You can subtract large numbers by counting up in steps.

```
    2 5 0
  -   8 9
        1   (to make 90)
      1 0   (to make 100)
    1 0 0   (to make 200)
      5 0   (to make 250)
Add them all up:  1 6 1
```

Subtract these numbers. Write the steps and then the answers.

```
  2 6 5
-   7 7
      3   (to make 80)
    2 0   (to make 100)
  1 0 0   (to make 200)
    6 5   (to make 265)
  1 8 8
```

```
  3 4 7
-   5 9
      1   (to make 60)
    4 0   (to make 100)
  2 0 0   (to make 300)
    4 7   (to make 347)
  2 8 8
```

```
  4 5 2
-   6 8
      2   (to make 70)
    3 0   (to make 100)
  3 0 0   (to make 400)
    5 2   (to make 452)
  3 8 4
```

```
  6 8 1
-   8 5
      5   (to make 90)
    1 0   (to make 100)
  5 0 0   (to make 600)
    8 1   (to make 681)
  5 9 6
```

Subtracting by borrowing 10

You can subtract large numbers by borrowing a 10.

```
    6 1
  2 7 0      0 – 9 is difficult, so borrow a 10.
-   3 9      The 70 becomes 60.
  2 3 1      10 – 9 = 1 and 60 – 30 = 30
```

Subtract these numbers.

```
  5 1
2 6 5
-  2 9
  236
```

```
  4 1
2 5 4
-  1 8
  236
```

```
  4 1
4 5 6
-  2 7
  429
```

```
  7 1
2 8 6
-  4 7
  239
```

```
  8 1
3 9 1
-  6 5
  326
```

```
  4 1
2 5 0
-  3 8
  212
```

```
  5 1
1 6 3
-  5 6
  107
```

```
  8 1
1 9 2
-  7 9
  113
```

```
  2 1
3 3 3
-  1 4
  319
```

Subtraction facts

Here are some families of subtraction facts. Write the missing numbers.
Look for patterns.

11 – 1 = $\boxed{10}$ 12 – 2 = $\boxed{10}$

$\boxed{11}$ – 2 = 9 $\boxed{12}$ – 3 = 9

11 – $\boxed{3}$ = 8   12 – $\boxed{4}$ = 8

11 – 4 = $\boxed{7}$ 12 – 5 = $\boxed{7}$

$\boxed{11}$ – 5 = 6 $\boxed{12}$ – 6 = 6

11 – $\boxed{6}$ = 5   12 – $\boxed{7}$ = 5

11 – 7 = $\boxed{4}$ 12 – 8 = $\boxed{4}$

$\boxed{11}$ – 8 = 3 $\boxed{12}$ – 9 = 3

11 – $\boxed{9}$ = 2   12 – $\boxed{10}$ = 2

11 – 10 = $\boxed{1}$ 12 – 11 = $\boxed{1}$

Counting on to subtract

When you subtract numbers, look at them first. If they are close
together you can quickly count on.
For example, if you have 502 – 499 it is quicker to count on from 499:

$$499: \quad \begin{matrix} & 1 & 2 & 3 \\ & 500, & 501, & 502 \end{matrix}$$

The answer is 3.

Count on to find the answers to these subtractions. Write your counting in
the long boxes.

701 – 699 = $\boxed{2}$ 412 – 408 = $\boxed{4}$

$\boxed{\text{699: 700, 701}}$ $\boxed{\text{408: 409, 410, 411, 412}}$

634 – 628 = $\boxed{6}$ 451 – 449 = $\boxed{2}$

$\boxed{\text{628: 629, 630, 631, 632, 633, 634}}$ $\boxed{\text{449: 450, 451}}$

872 – 867 = $\boxed{5}$ 733 – 728 = $\boxed{5}$

$\boxed{\text{867: 868, 869, 870, 871, 872}}$ $\boxed{\text{728: 729, 730, 731, 732, 733}}$

942 – 939 = $\boxed{3}$ 864 – 859 = $\boxed{5}$

$\boxed{\text{939: 940, 941, 942}}$ $\boxed{\text{859: 860, 861, 862, 863, 864}}$

Multiples of 10

When you add or subtract multiples of 10, only the hundreds and tens
change. There is always a 0 in the units place.

```
 HTU              HTU
  5 0            1 5 0
+ 7 0          –   7 0
-----          -------
1 2 0            8 0
```

Write the answers to these additions and subtractions.

40 + 80 = $\boxed{120}$ 160 – 70 = $\boxed{90}$

110 – 50 = $\boxed{60}$ 50 + 60 = $\boxed{110}$

60 + 60 = $\boxed{120}$ 130 – 80 = $\boxed{50}$

120 – 60 = $\boxed{60}$ 90 + 30 = $\boxed{120}$

50 + 80 = $\boxed{130}$ 170 – 70 = $\boxed{100}$

130 – 90 = $\boxed{40}$ 50 + 90 = $\boxed{140}$

90 + 40 = $\boxed{130}$ 160 – 80 = $\boxed{80}$

Three-digit numbers

When you subtract a one-digit number from a three-digit number,
sometimes the answer crosses back to the last 10.

$$184 – 9 = 175$$

It can help to work it out in two steps.

$$184 – 9 =$$
$$100 + (84 – 9) =$$
$$100 + (75) = 175$$

Write the answers to these subtractions.

375 – 7 = $\boxed{368}$ 354 – 8 = $\boxed{346}$

413 – 6 = $\boxed{407}$ 432 – 6 = $\boxed{426}$

523 – 8 = $\boxed{515}$ 721 – 9 = $\boxed{712}$

649 – 3 = $\boxed{646}$ 246 – 7 = $\boxed{239}$

756 – 9 = $\boxed{747}$ 633 – 5 = $\boxed{628}$

487 – 7 = $\boxed{480}$ 867 – 9 = $\boxed{858}$

525 – 6 = $\boxed{519}$ 764 – 8 = $\boxed{756}$

291 – 5 = $\boxed{286}$ 472 – 7 = $\boxed{465}$

Four-digit numbers

When you subtract a one-digit number from a four-digit number, sometimes the answer crosses back to the last 10.

2173 – 6 = 2167

It can help to work it out in two steps.

2173 – 6 =
2100 + (73 – 6) =
2100 + (67) = 2167

Write the answers to these subtractions.

3725 – 8 = [3717]   3594 – 5 = [3589]

4143 – 7 = [4136]   4342 – 4 = [4338]

5263 – 9 = [5254]   7261 – 2 = [7259]

6459 – 4 = [6455]   2436 – 9 = [2427]

7536 – 6 = [7530]   6323 – 6 = [6317]

4817 – 8 = [4809]   8657 – 7 = [8650]

5285 – 7 = [5278]   7684 – 8 = [7676]

2971 – 6 = [2965]   4792 – 3 = [4789]

Subtracting by taking too much

Another way to subtract is to take too much, like 100 in the example below, and then add the difference back on.

```
    2 5 6
  –   8 9
    1 5 6   (256 – 100)
  + 1 1     (difference between 100 and 89)
```
Add them all up: 1 6 7

Subtract these numbers. Write the steps and then the answers.

```
    2 3 4                       3 4 7
  –   7 5                     –   8 9
    1 3 4  (234 – 100)         2 4 7  (347 – 100)
  + 2 5    (difference)      + 1 1    (difference)
  [1 5 9]                     [2 5 8]
```

```
    5 4 1                       4 8 6
  –   5 7                     –   8 8
    4 4 1  (541 – 100)         3 8 6  (486 – 100)
  + 4 3    (difference)      + 1 2    (difference)
  [4 8 4]                     [3 9 8]
```

Subtracting by borrowing 100

You can subtract large numbers by borrowing a 100.

```
   3 1
   4̸3̸6    36 – 56 is difficult, so borrow a 100.
 –   5 6    The 400 becomes 300.
   3̲8̲0̲    6 – 6 = 0 and 130 – 50 = 80.
```

Subtract these numbers.

```
   1 1                    1 1
   2̸6 5                   2̸6 8
 –   9 2                –   7 2
  [1 7 3]                [1 9 6]
```

```
   1 1                    1 1
   2̸5 4                   2̸8 6
 –   8 1                –   9 4
  [1 7 3]                [1 9 2]
```

```
   2 1                    0 1
   3̸5 7                   1̸2 6
 –   7 3                –   8 3
  [2 8 4]                [4 3]
```

Using subtractions to check

If you add 25 and 35, you get 60.

25 + 35 = 60

To check the answer, you can take away.

60 – 25 = 35
60 – 35 = 25

Write the subtractions you can use to check these additions.

600 + 400 = 1000   [1000 – 400] = [600]
                     [1000 – 600] = [400]

36 + 35 = 71   [71 – 35] = [36]
                     [71 – 36] = [35]

49 + 33 = 82   [82 – 33] = [49]
                     [82 – 49] = [33]

65 + 35 = 100   [100 – 35] = [65]
                     [100 – 65] = [35]

120 + 380 = 500   [500 – 380] = [120]
                     [500 – 120] = [380]

Numbers ending in 9

When you subtract numbers ending in 9 from a three-digit number, it is usually quicker to change the 9 to the nearest 10 and then add 1 to the answer. For example:

$$136 - 9$$

$$136 - 10 = 126 \ (+1).$$ The answer is 127.

Subtract these numbers.

133 – 9 = ☐   242 – 29 = ☐

248 – 19 = ☐   565 – 29 = ☐

452 – 29 = ☐   456 – 19 = ☐

325 – 9 = ☐   388 – 9 = ☐

244 – 19 = ☐   167 – 19 = ☐

126 – 9 = ☐   542 – 29 = ☐

537 – 19 = ☐   263 – 19 = ☐

462 – 9 = ☐   371 – 9 = ☐

Subtracting hundreds

It is as easy to subtract hundreds numbers as it is to subtract units.
The answers always end in at least two zeros.

$$1400 - 700 = 700$$

Work out these subtractions.

1400 − 800 = ☐   1100 − ☐ = 200

1500 − 700 = ☐   1800 − ☐ = 900

1200 − ☐ = 300   1500 − 800 = ☐

1300 − ☐ = 500   1400 − 900 = ☐

1600 − 900 = ☐   1600 − ☐ = 800

1500 − 600 = ☐   1400 − ☐ = 700

1400 − ☐ = 500   1200 − 800 = ☐

1600 − ☐ = 900   1300 − 600 = ☐

1500 − 900 = ☐   1100 − ☐ = 800

1700 − 800 = ☐   1300 − ☐ = 600

Adding and subtracting

When you add two small numbers, sometimes they make more than 10. It can help to think of a pair of numbers that make 10 and break up the second number to make the pair.

$$6 + 7 = 13$$

$$6 + 4 (+ 3) = 10 + 3 = 13$$

When you subtract numbers, you can break up the second number to bring the bigger number down to 10.

$$13 - 5 = 8$$

$$(13 - 3) - 2 = 10 - 2 = 8$$

Write the answers to these problems. Look carefully at the signs.

5   +   8   =   ☐   11   –   ☐   =   7

5   +   ☐   =   14   16   –   8   =   ☐

7   +   8   =   ☐   ☐   –   7   =   4

9   +   ☐   =   17   17   –   9   =   ☐

5   +   7   =   ☐   16   –   ☐   =   9

8   +   ☐   =   12   14   –   6   =   ☐

7   +   6   =   ☐   ☐   –   9   =   9

Adding and subtracting

When you add a small number to a bigger number, sometimes they cross the next ten. It can help to break up the small number to take the bigger number up to the next ten:

$$34 + 8 = 42$$
$$(34 + 6) + 2 = 40 + 2 = 42$$

When you subtract numbers, you can also break up the small number to bring the bigger number down to the nearest ten:

$$72 - 9 = 63$$
$$(72 - 2) - 7 = 70 - 7 = 63$$

Write the missing numbers. Look carefully at the signs.

24 + 7 = ☐   63 – 5 = ☐

37 + ☐ = 42   46 – ☐ = 39

43 + 8 = ☐   54 – 6 = ☐

58 + ☐ = 65   81 – ☐ = 74

65 + 9 = ☐   35 – 7 = ☐

36 + ☐ = 41   74 – ☐ = 67

44 + 8 = ☐   92 – 9 = ☐

Subtracting 10, 100 or 1000

When you subtract 10 from a number, only the tens change.

$$5639 - 10 = 5629$$

When you subtract 100 from a number, only the hundreds change.

$$5639 - 100 = 5539$$

When you subtract 1000 from a number, only the thousands change.

$$5639 - 1000 = 4639$$

Write the answers to these questions.

What is 100 less than 3715? ☐

What is 10 less than 3715? ☐

What is 1000 less than 3715? ☐

What is 1000 less than 6423? ☐

What is 10 less than 8179? ☐

What is 100 less than 4812? ☐

What is 1000 less than 2184? ☐

Speed check

Subtract the numbers and write the answers. Work as quickly as you can.
Time yourself.

18 – 3 = ☐   19 – 4 = ☐   14 – 9 = ☐

16 – 9 = ☐   15 – 5 = ☐   12 – 6 = ☐

19 – 6 = ☐   17 – 8 = ☐   14 – 8 = ☐

20 – 7 = ☐   16 – 7 = ☐   17 – 9 = ☐

17 – 6 = ☐   18 – 9 = ☐   20 – 9 = ☐

13 – 7 = ☐   11 – 5 = ☐   15 – 6 = ☐

15 – 8 = ☐   16 – 6 = ☐   13 – 6 = ☐

16 – 8 = ☐   13 – 8 = ☐   18 – 8 = ☐

11 – 9 = ☐   14 – 7 = ☐   20 – 8 = ☐

17 – 5 = ☐   12 – 9 = ☐   13 – 9 = ☐

How long did this take you?   ☐

Subtracting large numbers

You can subtract large numbers by counting up in steps.

```
    2 5 0
 –   8 9
         1   (to make 90)
       1 0   (to make 100)
     1 0 0   (to make 200)
        5 0  (to make 250)
Add them all up:  1 6 1
```

Subtract these numbers. Write the steps and then the answers.

```
    2 6 5              3 4 7
 –   7 7            –   5 9
```

⬚   ⬚

```
    4 5 2              6 8 1
 –   6 8            –   8 5
```

⬚   ⬚

Subtracting by borrowing 10

When you subtract large numbers, you may need to borrow a 10.

$$
\begin{array}{r}
\overset{6\ 1}{2\ \cancel{7}\ 0} \\
-\ \ 3\ 9 \\
\hline
2\ 3\ 1
\end{array}
$$

0 – 9 is difficult, so borrow a 10.
The 70 becomes 60.
10 – 9 = 1 and 60 – 30 = 30

Subtract these numbers.

$$
\begin{array}{r}
2\ 6\ 5 \\
-\ \ \ 2\ 9 \\
\hline
\end{array}
\qquad
\begin{array}{r}
2\ 5\ 4 \\
-\ \ \ 1\ 8 \\
\hline
\end{array}
\qquad
\begin{array}{r}
4\ 5\ 6 \\
-\ \ \ 2\ 7 \\
\hline
\end{array}
$$

$$
\begin{array}{r}
2\ 8\ 6 \\
-\ \ \ 4\ 7 \\
\hline
\end{array}
\qquad
\begin{array}{r}
3\ 9\ 1 \\
-\ \ \ 6\ 5 \\
\hline
\end{array}
\qquad
\begin{array}{r}
2\ 5\ 0 \\
-\ \ \ 3\ 8 \\
\hline
\end{array}
$$

$$
\begin{array}{r}
1\ 6\ 3 \\
-\ \ \ 5\ 6 \\
\hline
\end{array}
\qquad
\begin{array}{r}
1\ 9\ 2 \\
-\ \ \ 7\ 9 \\
\hline
\end{array}
\qquad
\begin{array}{r}
3\ 3\ 3 \\
-\ \ \ 1\ 4 \\
\hline
\end{array}
$$

Subtraction facts

Here are some families of subtraction facts. Write the missing numbers.
Look for patterns.

11   –   1   =   ☐   12   –   2   =   ☐

☐   –   2   =   9   ☐   –   3   =   9

11   –   ☐   =   8   12   –   ☐   =   8

11   –   4   =   ☐   12   –   5   =   ☐

☐   –   5   =   6   ☐   –   6   =   6

11   –   ☐   =   5   12   –   ☐   =   5

11   –   7   =   ☐   12   –   8   =   ☐

☐   –   8   =   3   ☐   –   9   =   3

11   –   ☐   =   2   12   –   ☐   =   2

11   –   10   =   ☐   12   –   11   =   ☐

Counting on to subtract

When you subtract numbers, look at them first. If they are close together you can quickly count on.

For example, if you have 502 – 499 it is quicker to count on from 499:

$$\begin{array}{cccc} & 1 & 2 & 3 \\ 499: & 500, & 501, & 502 \end{array}$$

The answer is 3.

Count on to find the answers to these subtractions. Write your counting in the long boxes.

701 – 699 = ☐

412 – 408 = ☐

634 – 628 = ☐

451 – 449 = ☐

872 – 867 = ☐

733 – 728 = ☐

942 – 939 = ☐

864 – 859 = ☐

Multiples of 10

When you add or subtract multiples of 10, only the hundreds and tens change. There is always a 0 in the units place.

```
   HTU              HTU
    5 0            1 5 0
 +  7 0          -   7 0
 ———————        ———————
  1 2 0             8 0
```

Write the answers to these additions and subtractions.

40 + 80 = ☐   160 − 70 = ☐

110 − 50 = ☐   50 + 60 = ☐

60 + 60 = ☐   130 − 80 = ☐

120 − 60 = ☐   90 + 30 = ☐

50 + 80 = ☐   170 − 70 = ☐

130 − 90 = ☐   50 + 90 = ☐

90 + 40 = ☐   160 − 80 = ☐

Three-digit numbers

When you subtract a one-digit number from a three-digit number, sometimes the answer crosses back to the last 10.

$$184 - 9 = 175$$

It can help to work it out in two steps.

$$184 - 9 =$$
$$100 + (84 - 9) =$$
$$100 + (75) = 175$$

Write the answers to these subtractions.

375 – 7 = ☐   354 – 8 = ☐

413 – 6 = ☐   432 – 6 = ☐

523 – 8 = ☐   721 – 9 = ☐

649 – 3 = ☐   246 – 7 = ☐

756 – 9 = ☐   633 – 5 = ☐

487 – 7 = ☐   867 – 9 = ☐

525 – 6 = ☐   764 – 8 = ☐

291 – 5 = ☐   472 – 7 = ☐

Four-digit numbers

When you subtract a one-digit number from a four-digit number, sometimes the answer crosses back to the last 10.

$$2173 - 6 = 2167$$

It can help to work it out in two steps.

$$2173 - 6 =$$
$$2100 + (73 - 6) =$$
$$2100 + (67) = 2167$$

Write the answers to these subtractions.

3725 − 8 = ☐   3594 − 5 = ☐

4143 − 7 = ☐   4342 − 4 = ☐

5263 − 9 = ☐   7261 − 2 = ☐

6459 − 4 = ☐   2436 − 9 = ☐

7536 − 6 = ☐   6323 − 6 = ☐

4817 − 8 = ☐   8657 − 7 = ☐

5285 − 7 = ☐   7684 − 8 = ☐

2971 − 6 = ☐   4792 − 3 = ☐

Subtracting by taking too much

Another way to subtract is to take too much, like 100 in the example below, and then add the difference back on.

```
    2 5 6
  -   8 9
    1 5 6   (256 – 100)
  +   1 1   (difference between 100 and 89)
Add them all up:  1 6 7
```

Subtract these numbers. Write the steps and then the answers.

```
    2 3 4              3 4 7
  -   7 5            -   8 9
```

```
    5 4 1              4 8 6
  -   5 7            -   8 8
```

30

Subtracting by borrowing 100

You can subtract large numbers by borrowing a 100.

$$
\begin{array}{r}
3\ 1 \\
\cancel{4}3\ 6 \\
-\quad 5\ 6 \\
\hline
3\ 8\ 0
\end{array}
$$

36 − 56 is difficult, so borrow a 100.
The 400 becomes 300.
6 − 6 = 0 and 130 − 50 = 80.

Subtract these numbers.

$$
\begin{array}{r}
2\ 6\ 5 \\
-\quad 9\ 2 \\
\hline
\end{array}
\qquad\qquad
\begin{array}{r}
2\ 6\ 8 \\
-\quad 7\ 2 \\
\hline
\end{array}
$$

$$
\begin{array}{r}
2\ 5\ 4 \\
-\quad 8\ 1 \\
\hline
\end{array}
\qquad\qquad
\begin{array}{r}
2\ 8\ 6 \\
-\quad 9\ 4 \\
\hline
\end{array}
$$

$$
\begin{array}{r}
3\ 5\ 7 \\
-\quad 7\ 3 \\
\hline
\end{array}
\qquad\qquad
\begin{array}{r}
1\ 2\ 6 \\
-\quad 8\ 3 \\
\hline
\end{array}
$$

Using subtractions to check

If you add 25 and 35, you get 60.

$$25 + 35 = 60$$

To check the answer, you can take away.

$$60 - 25 = 35$$

$$60 - 35 = 25$$

Write the subtractions you can use to check these additions.

$600 + 400 = 1000$ ⬚ = ⬚

⬚ = ⬚

$36 + 35 = 71$ ⬚ = ⬚

⬚ = ⬚

$49 + 33 = 82$ ⬚ = ⬚

⬚ = ⬚

$65 + 35 = 100$ ⬚ = ⬚

⬚ = ⬚

$120 + 380 = 500$ ⬚ = ⬚

⬚ = ⬚